Usborne
First Activities
Easter Fun

Fiona Watt
Illustrated by Katie Lovell

Photographs by Howard Allman
Digital manipulation by Nick Wakeford

Spring lambs

1. Draw a circle for a lamb's body with pink or lilac chalk and fill it in.

2. Draw a head, ears and four legs with a dark pencil. Add eyes and a nose.

3. Fill the head, ears and legs with purple chalk. Smudge the chalk a little with your finger.

4. Use white chalk to draw around and around on the lamb's back for fluffy wool.

You could draw a sheep with her newborn lambs.

Easter egg tag

1. Draw an egg on a small piece of thin cardboard.

2. Turn the cardboard over and paint it. Let the paint dry.

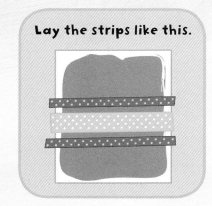

Lay the strips like this.

3. Cut small strips of ribbon and glue them onto the cardboard.

4. When the glue is dry, turn the cardboard over. Cut out the egg.

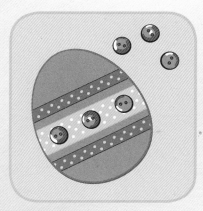

5. Glue on more decorations, such as buttons or sequins.

Use a hole puncher.

6. Punch a hole in the egg and thread some ribbon through.

You could draw stripes with a pencil.

You could fingerprint spots.

This egg had glitter sprinkled on while the paint was still wet.

Bunny card

Don't cut the fold.

1. Fold a rectangle of thin cardboard in half. Draw a shape for a body against the fold, like this.

2. Draw a shape for a head on another piece of cardboard. Add two long ears.

3. Cut around the shapes. Then, put the piece for the body to the side.

Pull the legs apart
to make the card stand up.

Let the
glue dry.

4. Cut shapes for a nose, cheeks and ears from pieces of material. Glue them onto the head.

5. When the glue is dry, draw two eyes and a little mouth with a pen.

6. Glue the head onto the body. Then, glue on a piece of a cotton ball, for a tail.

7

Butterfly garland

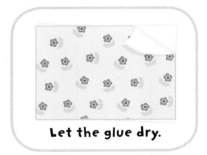

Let the glue dry.

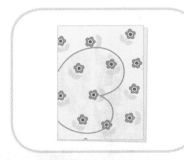

Don't cut here.

1. Cut two rectangles of patterned paper and glue them back to back.

2. Fold the paper in half and draw a butterfly wing against the fold.

3. Holding the paper together, carefully cut out the wing.

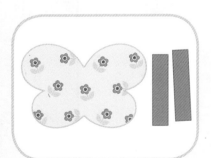

Let the glue dry.

4. Open out the wings. Then, cut two strips from thick paper for the body.

5. Glue the strips onto the wings, one on either side, to make the body.

6. Use a hole puncher to make holes in the body, one in either end.

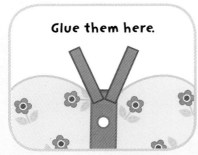

Glue them here.

7. Glue on two smaller strips of paper for feelers.

8. Use different scraps of patterned paper to make more butterflies.

9. Thread a long piece of string through the holes to make a garland.

Hen collage

Let the paint dry.

1. **Paint lots of spots on one piece of paper and stripes on another one.**

2. **Draw a shape for a hen on the spotted paper. Cut it out and glue it onto a piece of thick paper.**

3. **Draw a wing and some tail feathers on the striped paper. Cut them out.**

To make a nest,
glue strips of paper
overlapping each other.
Then, cut out eggs and
glue them on top.

4. Draw a beak,
legs and feathers
for the head on
some plain paper.
Cut them out, too.

5. Glue all the
pieces onto the
hen. Then, use
a pen to draw
an eye.

6. Cut some
strips of paper
for grass and
glue them
around the hen.

Printed chick

Print some wings, too.

1. Cut a triangle from a piece of sponge. Then, pour yellow paint onto an old plate.

2. Dip the sponge into the paint, then press it onto a piece of thick paper.

3. Press it onto the paper again and again to make a circle for the chick's body.

12

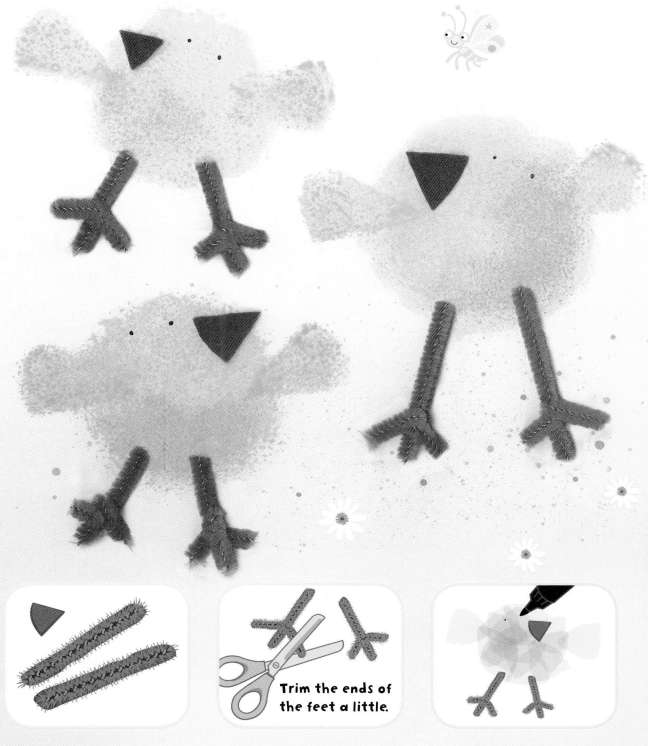

4. Cut a beak from some orange material. Then, cut two pieces of pipe cleaner.

5. Twist one piece around the other to make a foot. Make another foot in the same way.

Trim the ends of the feet a little.

6. Glue the beak and legs onto the body. Then, draw two little dots for eyes.

13

Springtime tree

1. Paint a tree trunk with pale pink paint on thick paper.

2. Using pale green paint, add an oval at the top of the trunk and fill it in.

Let the paint dry.

3. Use a thinner brush to paint some little leaves and grass, too.

4. Mix watery pink, green and white paints on an old plate.

5. Dip your finger in the paints and print lots of little dots for flowers.

The smaller dots on this tree were printed with the end of a paintbrush.

Easter basket

1. Draw a basket and a handle on a piece of light brown paper.

2. Draw lots of lines across the basket with a brown pencil.

3. Cut out the shapes. Glue them onto another piece of paper.

4. Cut a flower from a piece of material. Glue it onto the basket.

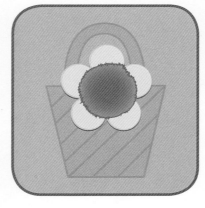

5. Cut a circle from another piece of material and glue it on.

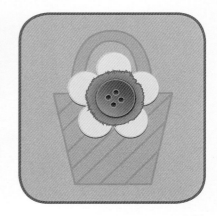

6. Glue on an old button for the middle of the flower.

You could glue
a basket onto
the front of an
Easter card.

Try making lots of
different shapes
of baskets.

This basket has
eggs cut from
material. The
basket was glued
on top of them.

Hanging bird

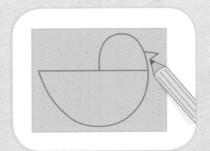

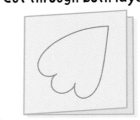

Cut through both layers.

1. Draw half a circle for a bird's body on bright paper. Add a head and a beak.

2. Cut out the bird. Then, erase any pencil lines.

3. Fold another piece of paper in half. Draw a wing and cut it out.

18

Glue the wings like this.

4. Make a hole in the bird's back using a hole puncher.

5. Push some thread through the hole for hanging.

6. Spread glue along the edge of each wing and press them on.

Crocus cards

1. Draw a flower with three petals on a piece of thick purple paper. Cut it out.

2. Carefully fold down the middle of each petal, along the dotted lines shown here.

3. Then, make a fold between each petal to make a shape, like this.

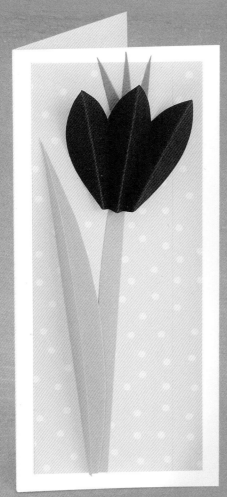

This card had a piece of patterned paper glued on first.

You could glue several crocuses onto one card.

Keep the paper folded as you cut.

These will be the stamens.

4. Fold a long piece of green paper in half and cut a thin leaf against the fold.

5. Cut a stem from green paper. Cut three small strips from orange paper, too.

6. Fold some paper for a card. Glue on the stem, leaf and stamens. Then, glue the flower on top.

Chocolate nests

For 12 nests you will need:

- A non-stick muffin tray with 12 holes
- 200g or 1 cup milk chocolate chips or chocolate broken into chunks
- 100g or ½ cup dark chocolate chips or chocolate broken into chunks
- 50g or ¼ cup butter
- 2 tablespoons runny honey
- 100g (4 cups) corn flakes

If you use a cup for measuring, use the same cup for each ingredient.
Store the nests in an airtight container and eat within four days.

Stir with a wooden spoon.

1. Add the butter and honey to a large pan. Gently melt them over a low heat.

2. Turn off the heat and add the chocolate. Keep stirring until the it has melted.

3. Gently stir in the corn flakes until they are coated in the chocolate mixture.

Press down lightly with a spoon.

4. To make the nests, spoon the mixture into the holes in the muffin tray.

5. Push three little chocolate eggs gently into the middle of each nest.

6. Chill the nests for one hour, then use a spoon to lift the nests out of the tray.

23

Easter bouquet

You need to press quite hard.

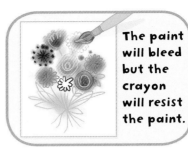
The paint will bleed but the crayon will resist the paint.

1. Using bright wax crayons, draw a bunch of flowers on thick paper.

2. Mix some watery paints in old pots. Brush your picture with clean water.

3. While the paint is wet, paint the leaves and dot bright paint onto each flower.

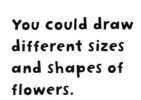

4. When the paint is dry, draw some more flowers and petals with felt-tip pens.

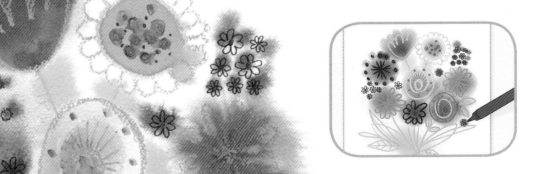

You could draw different sizes and shapes of flowers.